Religious Education
in the Classroom

Christianity
and
Other World Faiths

by
E. Freedman and J. Keys

Published by
Prim-Ed Publishing

2852
REV–03/04

Foreword

This series of books aims to provide teachers with a wide variety of activities which will support the Religious Education curriculum, whether Model 1 or Model 2 is being used. The materials will help develop knowledge and understanding of what it means to be a member of a faith community and how the teachings of these religions relate to shared human experience.

The activities were written to cover the attainment targets recommended for inclusion in an agreed syllabus.

Attainment Target 1: Learning about Religion

This includes the ability to:

- identify, name, describe and give accounts, in order to build a coherent picture of each religion;

- explain the meanings of religious language, stories and symbols; and

- explain similarities and differences between, and within, religions.

Attainment Target 2: Learning from Religion

This includes the ability to:

- give an informed and considered response to religious and moral issues;

- reflect on what might be learnt from religions in the light of one's own beliefs and experience; and

- identify and respond to questions of meaning within religions.

The materials aim to offer a coverage of the skills and processes in Religious Education, namely: investigation; interpretation; reflection; empathy; evaluation; analysis; synthesis; application; and expression. They can be used for whole class investigations and discussions, or by groups and pairs to engage in further research.

Fifty per cent of the activities within each book engage with Christianity; the remaining activities cover Buddhism, Hinduism, Islam, Judaism and Sikhism.

Contents

Teachers Notes
Christianity

1. and 2. The Christmas Story

The 'Christmas Story' is in both Luke (2:1-20) and Matthew (2:1-12). In John there is a poem about Jesus being the 'Word' and the 'Light' and in Mark, usually held to be the earliest of the gospels there is no story of Jesus' birth. The popular 'Christmas Story' is a combination of Luke and Matthew. They both agree that Jesus was born in Bethlehem and was the Messiah, this is based on Jewish scripture. Luke makes the point of Jesus being born in a poor and humble place, and his first visitors were shepherds, often considered to be outcasts, and has angels announcing the birth. Matthew has more references to the divine plan, and has the wise men led by a star, but they go first to Jerusalem and don't arrive until the Epiphany.

Split the class into two groups, one with Luke's gospel and the other with Matthew. Have them write the 'story' in six scenes, illustrate it and put it up for display.

The discussion of the differences between the 'stories' can be before or after the pupils complete the second worksheet, some boxes can be left blank for teachers or pupils to add other possible points of difference. The discussion should include some mention of timing, particularly of the visits and of the modern interpretation of the Gospels.

3. and 4. Changes in a Week

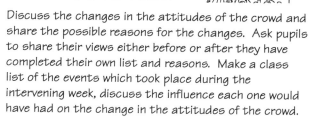

Read the biblical passages pertaining to the two incidents:

Palm Sunday - Mark 11; John 12
The Road to Golgotha - Mark 15

Discuss the changes in the attitudes of the crowd and share the possible reasons for the changes. Ask pupils to share their views either before or after they have completed their own list and reasons. Make a class list of the events which took place during the intervening week, discuss the influence each one would have had on the change in the attitudes of the crowd.

You could split the class into two groups, each to explore one of the days.

The group looking at Palm Sunday could share the G K Chesterton poem *The Donkey*, this will give one view of Palm Sunday. Ask the children to think of other views of the day.

The group looking at Good Friday could read the story of Simon, a visitor from Cyrene in North Africa (Mark 15) or of the other two crucified with Jesus.

5. The Disciples Word Grid

Before completing the word search, read the biblical reference to 'the fisher of men' (Mark 1,2,3) to the pupils. There are a number of good class discussions:

Why was it important for Christ to have disciples?

Why were there twelve disciples?
(There are 12 tribes of Israel.)

Did other religions have disciples?

What would have happened to Christianity if Christ hadn't had any disciples?

Who are the disciples of Christianity today?

How did other religions spread their teachings?

6. The Life of Jesus

The children could read the biblical passages pertaining to each illustration.

1. *John Baptises Jesus - Matthew 3*
2. *Jesus preaching - Matthew 5/Luke 6*

3. *Jesus in the temple - Mark 11*
4. *The last supper - John 13/Mark 14*
5. *Peter denies Jesus - Luke 22/John 18*
6. *The empty tomb - John 20*

In each case they should think about what the passage and the illustration are trying to say to us, what the relevance is today. It would be worthwhile to give pupils time to discuss their ideas before they complete the worksheet. Also, in what way are any of these events in the life of Jesus remembered today.

7. The Bible

This page is meant to be an introduction to the Bible. It would be useful to have a number of copies of different versions in the classroom for children to handle.

note: Christians believe that the new Testament is the completion of the Old Testament. Although the Old Testament is the same words as the Torah it is not helpful to make direct comparison between the two books. The Torah is in Hebrew, it is written on scrolls and is read in the synagogue in a regular cycle, to ensure it is all read.

Teachers Notes

8. The Books of the Bible

Children need to access a copy of the Bible, so they can fill in all of the names.

The Old Testament

Law – Genesis, Exodus, Leviticus, Numbers, Deuteronomy

History – Joshua, Judges, Ruth, 1 Samuel, 2 Samuel, 1 Kings, 2 Kings, 1 Chronicles, 2 Chronicles, Ezra, Nehemiah, Esther

Wisdom – Job, Psalms, Proverbs, Ecclesiastes, Song of Songs

Prophecy – Isiah, Jeremiah, Lamentations, Ezekiel, Daniel, Hosea, Hoel, Amos, Obadiah, Jonah, Micah, Nahum, Habakkuk, Zephaniah, Haggai, Zachariah, Malachi

The New Testament

History – Matthew, Mark, Luke, John, Acts of the Apostles

Letters – Romans, 1 Corinthians, 2 Corinthians, Galatians, Ephesians, Phillippians, Colossians, 1 Thessalonians, 2 Thessalonians, 1 Timothy, 2 Timothy, Titus, Philemon, Hebrews, James, 1 Peter, 2 Peter, 1 John, 2 John, 3 John, Jude

Prophecy – Revelations

Encourage them to choose a different book from which to choose their story.

9. Old Testament People

Children will need access to a bible, to see if they can find the stories. A children's bible will be easier, as it will have illustrations which may help.

Here are some references for each character, they are not the only one, however, as some characters have many references.

Noah – Genesis 6-9
Joseph – Genesis 37-42
Moses – Exodus 2
Ruth – Ruth
David – 1 Samuel 17
Esther – Esther

10. New Testament Stories

As some of the interesting references sometimes include more than one incident, the suggested incident is listed below.

Mark 5 - The raising of Jairus's daughter

Matthew 14 - Jesus walks on the water

Luke 19 - Zacchaeus and Jesus

Acts 9:3-19 - The conversion of Saul

Children can select stories for others to find references, or give references for others in the group to find the stories.

11. New Testament Places

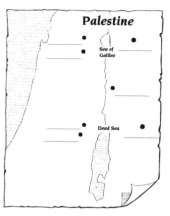

The places on the map are:

1. Luke 7 - Capermaum
2. Mark 1 - Sea of Galilee
3. John 2 - Cana
4. Luke 1 - Nazareth
5. Matthew 3 - River Jordan
6. Mark 11 - Jerusalem
7. Luke 2 - Bethlehem
8. Matthew 1 - Jericho

Note: A map of Palestine in the time of Christ can usually be found in the back of the Bible.

12. The Bible Survey

Before completing this survey children could, in groups, complete tick sheets to help them collect the data. The books on worksheet 8 would help in this. Each group could create the tick sheet for a different set of questions. If children use a tick sheet, they could then create a graph showing which books, stories, etc. are the best known and the number of votes each respective book, story, etc. receives.

	10 or more do	5 to 10 do	1 to 5 do	No-one does
Do you know the number of books in the Bible?				
Can you name one group of books in the Old Testament?				
Can you name 10 books in the Old Testament?				
Can you name 5 stories from the Old Testament?				
Can you name 2 Psalms?				
Can you name the 4 Gospels?				
Can you name 5 other books in the New Testament?				
Can you name 2 miracles in the New Testament?				
Can you name 2 parables in the New Testament?				
Can you name the 12 Apostles?				

The survey sheet can be altered with a correction pen, to change the number of books, etc., or to add in different questions.

Teachers Notes

13. The Orthodox Church

In 1054 there was a dispute between the two heads of the church in Constantinople (The Patriarch) and Rome (The Pope). There were two parts to the church at this time because the Roman Empire had split in two. This disagreement became known as The Great Schism. The two branches have gone their own way with some differences in belief and worship. The Nicene creed which came out of the council at Nicaea called by Constantine in 325 is a central Christian doctrine, it predates the Great Schism and is therefore part of both the Orthodox and Western branches of Christianity. Today the Greek and Russian Orthodox churches are the main groups in the Orthodox religion, and there are differences between the two. They both celebrate Christmas and Easter, although not always at the same time, because of the different calendars in use. The Greek Orthodox Church celebrates Christmas on 25 December, but the Russian Orthodox Church celebrates it on 6 January. The various calendars may be a project of interest to some pupils.

It would be useful for children to either visit an Orthodox Church or to look at photographs of one.

Once children have drawn their illustrations the labelling is very important, as this can be used as a platform for a comparison chart with other 'Western' Christian Churches. Also, children in groups could draw the inside of other churches and label them, creating a series of illustrations for discussion.

14. Places of Worship

If possible it is advantageous to visit a number of churches. One thing to bear in mind is that churches from many denominations have changed over the years, for example; in an older Methodist or Baptist church the pulpit would have dominated the church, in a Roman Catholic Church the old altar may still be on the wall, with the new altar facing the congregation.

Some of the words used fit with more than one denomination.

The suggested linking is:

Anglican: lectern, altar, font

Baptist: pool, pulpit, table

Methodist: organ, 'empty' cross, pulpit

Roman Catholic: tabernacle, confessional, statues

Quaker: table, bible, seats 'in the round'

15. The Christian Year

It may be useful to undertake this sheet as a pair or group activity. The Christian Year does have two cycles within it, the Christmas and the Easter cycle. The Christmas cycle is solar and the Easter cycle is lunar. Therefore, children should concentrate on one or the other of the cycles and bring the information together. It is a good opportunity to look in more detail at some of the other celebrations in the Christian Year.

16. Christian Values

The most important part of this activity is the discussion. Children should talk to a committed Christian first, this could be an activity undertaken at home or in the community. An interview sheet may be helpful and could be worked up as a class activity.

Other words can be added to the sheet, or those on the sheet could be deleted and replaced by others. There are no correct answers, the discussion should bring an added dimension to children's understanding of these values.

17. A Christian Organisation

This sheet may be best undertaken in small groups, each looking at a different organisation. If the children cannot visit the organisation, invite a member from each organisation into the school. The class could work on an interview sheet together, as the same questions could be asked of each organisation. The organisation should be local, so children can relate to it. In this instance it should be a 'Christian' organisation and not a charity. Therefore, a church should be the focus. (A charity could be looked at separately and the central values compared.)

It is important to have the children think about the people in the organisation, as, presumably, at least some of them are volunteers.

An extension to this could be that the group makes a diary of the organisation events, or a poster 'selling' the services of the organisation to the class, school or community. In this later activity, the Christian values of the organisation should be central to the poster.

Teachers Notes

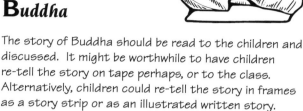

18. The Apostles Creed

The two 'Creeds' are very important to Christians, as reaffirmation of their beliefs. The Nicene Creed is very long, most Christians know the beginning:

We believe in one God, the Father, the Almighty, maker of Heaven and Earth, of all that is seen and unseen. We believe in one Lord, Jesus Christ, the only Son of God.

The children could research the whole Nicene Creed and write it up for a class discussion or a comparison with the Apostles' Creed.

The Nicene Creed predates the Great Schism and is therefore adopted by all Christians.

The Apostles' Creed talks of the 'Catholic' church which in this instance meant 'universal', as this was written before the 'Protestant' churches broke away from Rome.

19. Saint Francis of Assisi

Saint Francis is a very interesting story, which children could investigate further, also the story of Saint Claire who was a friend of Francis and started the Poor Claire order of nuns. This could extend to a discussion of patron saints, or group investigations of other saints, such as Saint Christopher.

20. Committed Christians

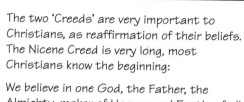

Children should discuss their findings on Martin Luther King and Bishop Desmond Tutu before writing on the sheet. This will help them to translate the values into the deeds. The third person should, ideally, be someone from the community. However, if this is not possible a national person could be used. The advantage of a local person would be the opportunity to talk to the person directly. Children could work in groups and take a different person for each group, then make a poster for display.

Buddhism

21. Buddha

The story of Buddha should be read to the children and discussed. It might be worthwhile to have children re-tell the story on tape perhaps, or to the class. Alternatively, children could re-tell the story in frames as a story strip or as an illustrated written story.

It is important children understand that Buddha was a good man who set an example for others, which they still try to follow, while seeking the enlightenment he achieved. One of the important premises of Buddhism is to alleviate suffering for all living creatures.

When the children think about how they can relieve suffering pets and other animals should be included in addition to friends, relations and others.

22. The Five Promises

There are no rules in Buddhism but Buddhists understand that everything they do has its own result, so they try to make sensible choices. They believe that bad choices will affect not only themselves but also many others. The five 'promises', or precepts, help them to remember to act well.

This exercise asks children to think about these precepts of the religion and how they could achieve them in their own lives. This should give some understanding of the Buddhist way.

This exercise could also be undertaken with the 'four noble truths':

total satisfaction is not possible, we must all suffer;

people suffer, often through their own greed;

desire and attachment can be overcome; and

the eight-fold path helps to overcome them.

The eight-fold path could also be looked at in this way. It was suggested by Buddha as the Middle Way, a code for living while searching for enlightenment. It is:

understanding what you want to do with your life;

thinking about how to follow the four noble truths;

saying good things;

acting wisely and living honestly;

working in jobs which will not hurt other living creatures;

making an effort to meet the difficulties;

being mindful of what you are doing, not being distracted;

and meditating to achieve nirvana.

Teachers Notes

23. Buddhist Teachings

Buddhists do not pray to a God, or to the prophet Buddha, so it is important children understand that their 'praying' is within themselves. When they 'pray' it is to the deepest part of themselves, based on what Buddha taught them.

The shrines and temples can be looked at in conjunction with the places of worship for other religions, but as there is no ritual as in other religions there are more differences from one to another than there are similarities.

24. Buddhist Pilgrimage

Pilgrimages are popular in Buddhist countries. Buddha was an important prophet and many Buddhists want to visit the places which were important in his life. These pilgrimages help the pilgrims to think about the life of Buddha and the way in which he lived his life. He lived his life in India and pilgrims come from over the world to these places.

It is important to draw the parallels with the pilgrimages of other religions, including those to the places where Jesus Christ lived his life.

Hinduism

25. Hindu Gods and Goddesses

The most important thing for children to grasp is that all Hindu gods and goddesses are part of the one supreme God, Brahman. There are three main gods; Brahma, the Creator; Vishnu, the Preserver; and Shiva, who is responsible for death and rebirth. Hindus often worship one of these three gods. Vishnu has ten avatars (incarnations), the two best known being Krishna and Rama. Krishna has a very large following, and Rama and his wife Sita are known because of their association with Divali. Ganesha is the son of Shiva and his wife Parvati; and Kali is one of the goddesses associated with Shiva.

Children could be asked to look at these and other pictures of the gods and goddesses and work out what the artefacts with which they are always represented mean. This would be a good topic for discussion, prior to children writing about the deity they most identify with and why.

26. Hinduism

This story comes from one of the Hindus' most important books, the Upanishads.

It is important children understand that Hinduism is multi-faceted. This story helps to explain that. Prior to doing the worksheet, children could have a feely-bag and try to describe different objects. Did children describe the same object differently? Can they think of objects which might be described differently if you touched a different part of it?

One important fact is that Hinduism often considers leaders of other faiths, (Buddha, Jesus or Muhammad as avatars of Vishnu.)

27. Hindu Worship

There is no imperative in Hinduism to visit the Mandir (temple), as there is in other religions. Hindus are free to go whenever they like. Often it is for social as much as religious reasons. The temple is the house where the god lives, and the god is like an honoured guest. The god is looked after like a close relation. There are various ceremonies during the day. The god is woken at dawn, there is food at meal times and the god goes to bed at night. Worship in the home is very important and the household shrine is kept scrupulously clean and well tended. Children might like to adopt a god and have a classroom shrine for a short time.

28. Benares

The pilgrimage to Benares brings together two important parts of Hindu worship, water and fire.

Children could plan a journey to Benares from a number of different places, for example, Britain, Sri Lanka or Southern India. This would give some understanding of the undertaking, particularly for poor people without access to high-speed transport.

Teachers Notes

Islam

29. Islam - Prophets and Beliefs

After the name of the prophet Muhammad is written or said, Muslims will write or say 'peace and blessings of Allah upon him'. After the names of the other prophets they will say or write 'peace be upon him'. It is important children understand this form of respect.

This will stimulate possible interest in the comparisons of the stories of the prophets from the three religions. It could also be worth discussing the similarities between the call of Moses and the call of Muhammad. Children could look at the prophets of each of the religions in groups and make comparisons.

30. Muslim Worship

The times of prayer are very important to Muslims, as is the washing prior to it. Children could plot the prayer times on a 24-hour clock, and compare it to their own daily routines. Comparing the difference between summer and winter might also promote discussion.

The correct order for the washing is:

1. Wash both hands.
2. Wash mouth.
3. Wash nostrils and nose.
4. Wash face.
5. Wash arms.
6. Wash head.
7. Wash ears.
8. Wash neck.
9. Wash feet.

31. The Mosque

If it is possible, take children to see a mosque. They will be able to see for themselves the features of the building and how they are part of the worship and how the building reflects the beliefs of the religion. Each feature should be discussed, so that these points can be raised. Children may notice there are no pictures, statues, etc. inside the mosque. The mosque is empty so nothing comes between a person and God.

A comparison between the people who lead the worship, the mu'adhin and the imam and the rabbi or priest, would also help children to understand the various roles.

32. The Hajj

It is important to give children a sense of excitement about the hajj. It is a big undertaking in the life of a Muslim. It may be planned for a long time and may involve hardship and sacrifice. It used to be a very long and perilous journey, although modern transport has shortened the time and increased the comfort of the journey. Mecca was an important city for Jews and Christians, but now only Muslims can visit Mecca. This was the city to which Muhammad went to restore the Ka'bah to the worship of the one God, therefore all Muslims want to follow in his footsteps.

Part of the hajj is the festival of Eid-al-Adha, the festival of sacrifice. This is celebrated out of Mecca at Mina. Here it is believed Abraham (Ibraham) was prepared to sacrifice his son, before God provided a ram. This festival shows that sacrifice should be part of a Muslim's life.

Judaism

33. Prophets and Teachers

This could be done as a group exercise, with each group taking a different prophet or teacher. They should read the story of the person and then discuss the important events, choosing the one they think is the most important, and being able to justify their choice. It is important to have a copy of the Jewish Bible, as it may differ slightly from the Christian Old Testament.

It is important to share the decisions children make in saying what relevance these incidents might have in their lives.

34. Jewish Customs and Traditions

This sheet asks children to focus on the customs and traditions which are important features of Jewish life. It is important to discuss the reasons for the ceremonies, and why Jews continue to follow the traditions. If possible, ask a local Rabbi to come and speak to the children. It might be worthwhile to discuss the difference between an Orthodox observance and a Liberal observance.

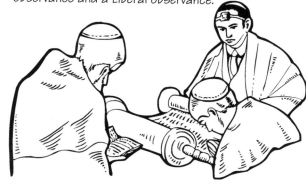

Teachers Notes

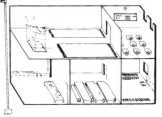

35. The Synagogue

If possible, take children to see a synagogue. They will then be able to see for themselves the features of the building and how they are part of the worship and how the building reflects the beliefs of the religion. Each feature should be discussed, so that these points can be raised. Children may notice that like the mosque there are no pictures, statues, etc. The second of the Ten Commandments forbids images of God.

A comparison between the people who lead the worship - the mu'adhin and the imam and the rabbi or priest - would also help children to understand the various roles.

36. Clothes for Prayer

These clothes are part of the Orthodox way of life. Again, a comparison between Orthodox and Liberal interpretation would be a worthwhile discussion.

If possible, have the artefacts in the classroom for children to see and touch, while engendering respect for these artefacts.

Sikhism

37. Sikh Gurus

Any reference on the Sikh religion will contain a list of the 10 Gurus and the book which has become the 11th Guru.

In the wordsearch the word Guru has not been used and where the name is two words, they have been run together.

38. The Khalsa

This is an important part of Sikh life. Unlike other religions, Sikhs choose to join or not, at any time in their lives. It will be interesting for children to compare the original reason for the foundation of the brotherhood with its part in Sikh life today.

39. The Gurdwara

If possible, take children to see a Gurdwara. They will then be able to see for themselves the features of the building and how they are part of the worship and how the building reflects the beliefs of the religion. Each feature should be discussed, so that these points can be raised.

40. Amritsar

Children should find Amritsar on the map. The town grew up around the pool and the temple. The four places of pilgrimage in India are very special for the Sikhs, because they are places of authority.

Glossaries

41. to 46. Glossaries

On each of these six pages are words associated with the six religions covered in this book. Children should use information books to find the meanings of the words if they do not know them already. This will help them to develop their knowledge of the vocabulary associated with each faith, in addition to developing their research skills. The sheets can be completed together as a project and made into a book, or with the other sheets covering the specific religion. The work can be undertaken individually, in pairs or as a group project.

Other words can be added to the sheets to increase the vocabulary children have at their disposal when discussing one of these religions.

Teachers Notes

World Religions

47. Books and Writings

All the religions in this book have sacred writings or scriptures which play an important part in the religion. However, they do not all have a 'book' which is the law or 'the Word of God'. There are three religions of 'the book' - Judaism, Islam and Christianity. In these three religions and in Sikhism the book plays an important role in the public acts of worship.

The Torah is a scroll kept in the ark in the synagogue. The scrolls used in the synagogue are hand-copied and a pointer is used, so the reader avoids touching the text. The Torah is also printed for use outside the synagogue. The Torah is the first five books of the Bible (Christians call this the Pentateuch). The Jewish Bible has two additional parts, the Prophets and the Writings, the whole Jewish Bible is sometimes called the Tenak.

The Qur'an is the word of Allah. It was revealed to Muhammad during the last 22 years of his life. Initially, it was passed on by word of mouth but then written down. It was not connected together until after the death of Muhammad. It is reverently studied in the mosque, although it does not have prominence there. The book is written in Arabic and is often highly decorated with calligraphy. Muslims believe the words of the Qur'an are God's revealed message.

The Christian Bible incorporated the Jewish Bible, referred to as the Old Testament, and the writings about the life and teachings of Jesus Christ, called the New Testament. The Bible is usually read at worship, often passages from both the Old Testament and the New Testament.

The Guru Granth Sahib has a special place in the Gurdwara, on a raised platform. For the Sikhs this is the eleventh and last guru. It is usually found only in the Gurdwara, few Sikhs would have a copy at home. It contains mainly prayers and hymns written by Guru Nanak and his successors.

Buddhists do not have one book. Most Buddhists would accept the Tripitaka (three baskets) as an important writing. It contains Buddha's sayings, comments on life and rules for monks. It was written during the 1st century BCE in Sri Lanka. The Dhammapada, or teaching verses, is one of the best known books of Theravada Buddhism and also contains Buddha's teachings, in shortened form. Verses of scripture are often chanted at Buddhist gatherings, particularly by monks.

47. Books and Writings cont...

Hinduism also has no one book, but many scriptures. The sacred writings of Hinduism were written in Sanskrit. The Vedas were passed on by word of mouth for centuries before being written down. One of the four Vedas, the Rig Veda, contains thousands of hymns. The Upanishads contains philosophical teachings about Brahman and the struggle to achieve nirvana. This is kept in the Mandir and read during some worship. The Ramayana contains the adventures of Rama and Sita. The Mahabharata is an epic poem telling of the struggle between two families. The most popular part of the Mahabharata is the Bhagavad Gita, which tells of a conversation between Krishna and his charioteer. The Gita is often used in meditation.

48. Festivals

Children should choose one festival from each religion and write about it, researching if necessary. This could be done as a pair activity. It is important that children try to focus on the reasons for the festival and how the celebrations try to reinforce the message. It could be worthwhile to discuss with children the similarities of some of the festivals, looking for the common threads, for example, the number of festivals held in mid-winter which focus on light. Another avenue for comparison might be the ways in which the Hindu festival of Divali differs from the Sikh festival.

note:

When dealing with religion other than Christianity it is customary not to use BC and AD for dates. BCE (Before the Common Era) is used for BC and CE (Common Era) for AD.

The Christmas Story 1

In your group, listen to the Christmas Story from the Bible. List the six important scenes in the story. Write each scene in your own words in the boxes below. Cut out each scene and illustrate it, making a wall frieze, a book or a display with your text and illustrations.

The Christmas Story 2

after you have heard the two Christmas stories complete this table showing the similarities and differences.

Luke 2:1-20

1.
2.
3.
4.
5.
6.
7.
8.
9.

Matthew 2:1-12

1.
2.
3.
4.
5.
6.
7.
8.
9.

1. What was the baby called?

2. In which town was the baby born?

3. Describe the place where the baby was born.

4. Why was the baby born in this place?

5. Who were the first visitors to see the baby?

6. When did they come to see the baby?

7. Was the birth of the baby announced?

8. How was it announced?

9. What is the main message of the text?

Changes in a Week 1

Look at the two pictures on this page. Write in the speech balloons what you think the people are saying.

On the next worksheet make a list of the changes in the attitude of the crowd between the two pictures. Write down why you think their attitudes have changed.

Changes in a Week 2

☆ Look at the pictures on the previous work sheet. Think about the changes in the attitude of the crowd during the week separating the two pictures. Write down what the changes are and why you think these changes occurred.

The changes in the attitude of the crowd, between Palm Sunday and Good Friday.

Reasons for the changes...

The Disciples Word Grid

Many people came to hear Jesus when he preached in Galilee, but he had twelve special followers called his disciples, or apostles. The first disciples were fishermen on the Sea of Galilee.

Andrew listened to Jesus and called his brother Simon to come and hear. Later Jesus gave Simon a new name, **Peter**, which means 'a rock'. Then two more fishermen, **James** and his brother **John,** came and listened. Then came **Matthew**, a tax collector, **Philip** from Bethsaida, **Nathaniel**, sometimes called Bartholomew, from Cana and **Simon** the Zealot. They were followed by **James,** the son of Alphaeus, **Thomas**, **Judas,** sometimes called Thaddeus, and **Judas Iscariot** who betrayed Jesus.

✩ Can you find all twelve in this word search?

s	a	d	u	j	p	z	t	x	a
s	i	m	o	n	h	w	h	y	n
j	a	m	e	s	i	v	o	u	d
u	p	q	u	r	l	s	m	t	r
m	j	o	h	n	i	o	a	n	e
a	i	j	k	l	p	m	s	j	w
s	m	a	t	t	h	e	w	a	h
z	b	c	a	d	e	f	t	m	g
y	n	a	t	h	a	n	i	e	l
i	s	c	a	r	i	o	t	s	r

The Life of Jesus

☆ *Here are some events in the life of Jesus. How does each event teach us something or affect our lives? Write in the box under each picture what each event shows or teaches us in our lives.*

John baptises Jesus

Jesus preaching

Jesus in the temple

The last supper

Peter denies Jesus

The empty tomb

The Bible

Fill in the spaces in this passage with the words highlighted on this page.

The Bible is the most important book for _____[1]. The Bible is a

focal point for Christian _____[2], both public and private. In church services

the _____[3] usually stands when there is a reading from the

Bible. Many Christians attend Bible _____[4] groups and many families

have a copy in their homes. Christians believe it is through the Bible

that God _____[5] to us today.

study   English   churches   three   Abraham   versions   collection

The Bible is really a _____[6] of books, not one book. It

contains 66 books all together. There are 39 books in the Old Testament, which are split into

_____[7] groups; Law, History, Wisdom and Prophecy. The Old Testament

tells us the story of God's relationship with his chosen people, the

_____[8]. It tells the story of the

_____[9] of the world, and the story of Israel from the time of

_____[10], about 2 000 BC, through the slavery in Egypt and the

settlement in the _____[11] land. The Old Testament was originally

written in Hebrew.

worship   Israelites   beginning   James   speaks   Apostles

There are 27 books in the New Testament, which are split into _____[12] groups; History,

Letters and Prophecy. Four of the books which tell the history are the _____[13]

of Matthew, Mark, Luke and John, four of the _____[14]. The word Gospel

means 'Good News'. The New Testament tells us the story of the life of _____[15] and

includes the letters, 'epistles', the apostles wrote to the new _____[16] who

were following the teachings of Jesus after his death. The New Testament was originally written in Greek.

Jesus   promised   Tudor   Gospels   four   congregation   Christians

The Bible was first translated into _____[17] by William Tyndale

during _____[18] times; it was translated into Welsh by Bishop

Morgan very soon afterwards. Today there are many _____[19] of the Bible.

One of the most popular is the King _____[20] Bible, translated in the time of King James VI.

The Books of the Bible

Look at a copy of the Bible and write the name of each book on its spine below.

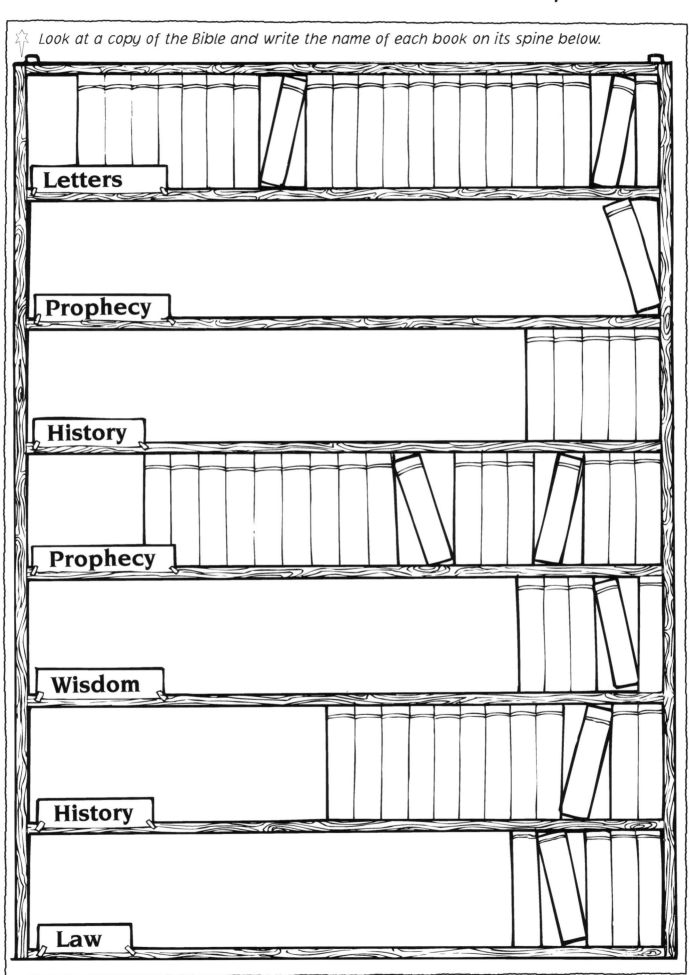

Old Testament People

☆ *Here are six people whose story you will find in the Old Testament. Find their story and write the biblical reference for each under their name.*

Noah	**Joseph**

Moses	**Ruth**

 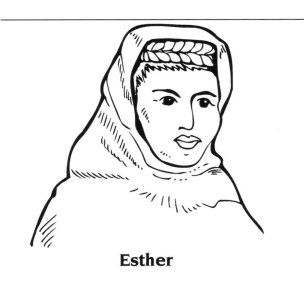

David	**Esther**

New Testament Stories

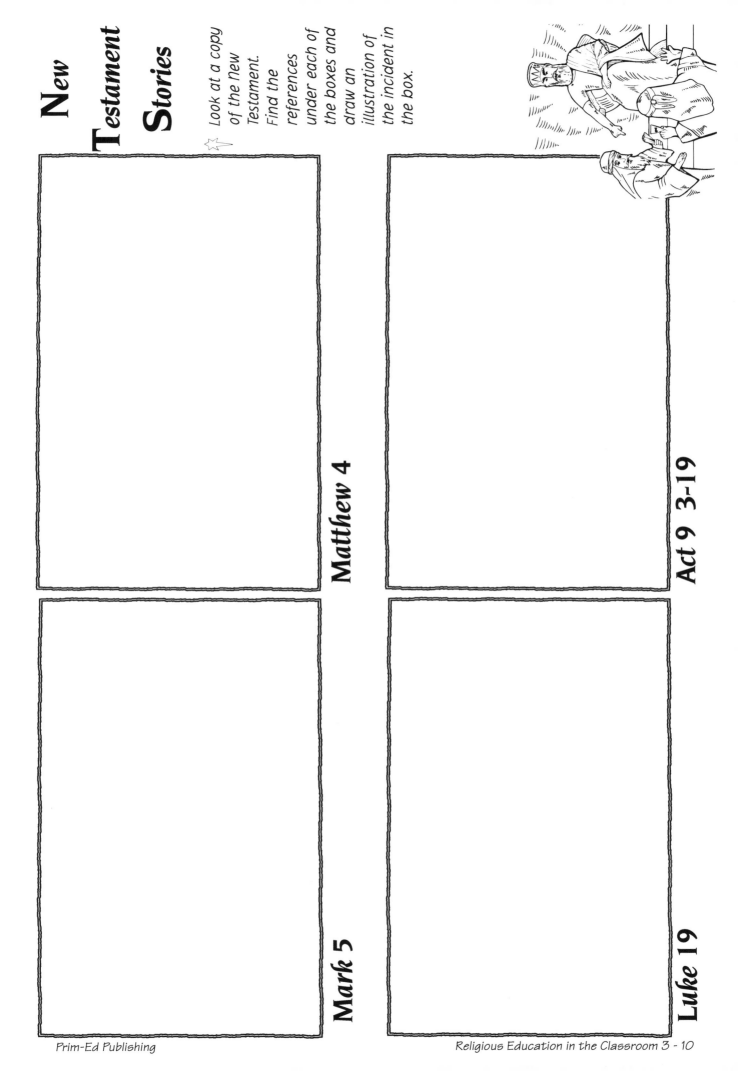

Look at a copy of the new Testament. Find the references under each of the boxes and draw an illustration of the incident in the box.

Matthew 4

Mark 5

Act 9 3-19

Luke 19

New Testament Places

On the map there are seven places marked. Look up the references below the map and write the place names and their number which are missing on the map.

Palestine

Sea of
Galilee

Dead Sea

1. Luke 7	2. Mark 1	3. John 2	4. Luke 1
5. Matthew 3	6. Mark 11	7. Luke 2	8. Matthew

A Bible Survey

☆ Ask 10 - 12 people the questions on this sheet. Share your results with your class.

	10 or more do	5 to 10 do	1 to 5 do	No-one does
Do you know the number of books in the Bible?				
Can you name one group of books in the Old Testament?				
Can you name 10 books in the Old Testament?				
Can you name 5 stories from the Old Testament?				
Can you name 2 Psalms?				
Can you name the 4 Gospels?				
Can you name 5 other books in the New Testament?				
Can you name 2 miracles in the New Testament?				
Can you name 2 parables in the New Testament?				
Can you name the 12 Apostles?				

The Orthodox Church

There are many different Christian denominations. They all share the same beliefs, but they do not believe exactly the same thing. They often worship in different ways.

The two main Christian groups are 'Orthodox' Christians and 'Western' Christians. In the days of the early Christian church, one group was based in Constantinople. This was the Eastern, or Orthodox, Church and the other group was based in Rome. This was the Western Church.

Read these statements about an Orthodox Church. Draw an illustration of an Orthodox Church during a service in the box. Label some important features. On a separate page, write how these features differ from a Western Christian Church.

When people enter an Orthodox Church they usually buy a candle. They light it and put it in front of an icon. They then make the sign of the cross. There are many icons in the church. An icon is a beautiful painting, often with gold leaf, of Jesus, the Virgin Mary and the Saints. During the service the congregation stand. A choir leads the singing. A priest leads the service. The altar is behind a screen which has doors in the middle. The priest is the only person who can go through the doors but they are open during the service.

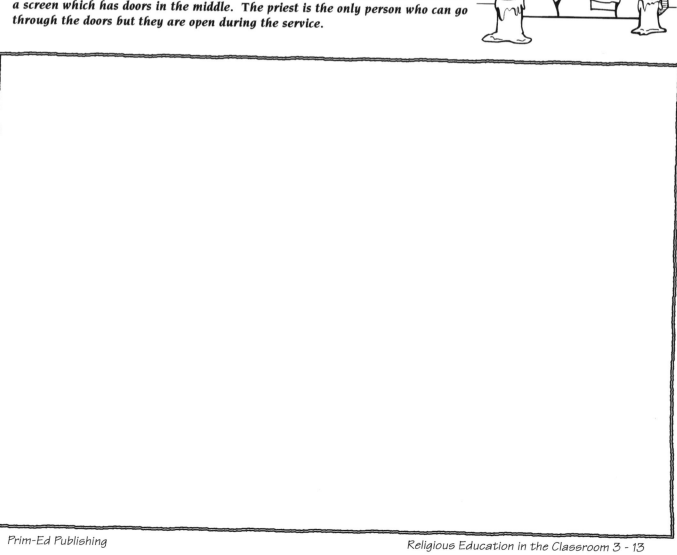

Places of Worship

There are many branches of Christianity within the 'Western' Christian church. The 'Protestant' churches broke away from the Catholic Church of Rome, in protest at some beliefs and forms of worship.

☆ These are all words we associate with *worship* for one of the Christian groups listed below. Write the words in the box in which you think they belong. Write a sentence to describe the worship of each group.

pool   font   table   bible   altar   organ

lectern   statues   tabernacle   confessional   'empty' cross   seats 'in the round'

pulpit

Christian Group	Words associated with their worship	A sentence describing their worship
Anglican		
Baptist		
Methodist		
Roman Catholic		
Quakers		

The Christian Year

The Christian Year is a cycle, and Christians focus on the important dates and celebrations. Some of the celebrations are fixed, Christmas is always on 25 December. Some are not fixed, Easter is between late March and late April. Ash Wednesday and Lent are fixed by the date of Easter because Lent is the forty days before Easter Sunday, excluding Sundays.

Here is a wheel showing the Christian Year. Can you put the names from the bottom of the page on the wheel, in the correct place?

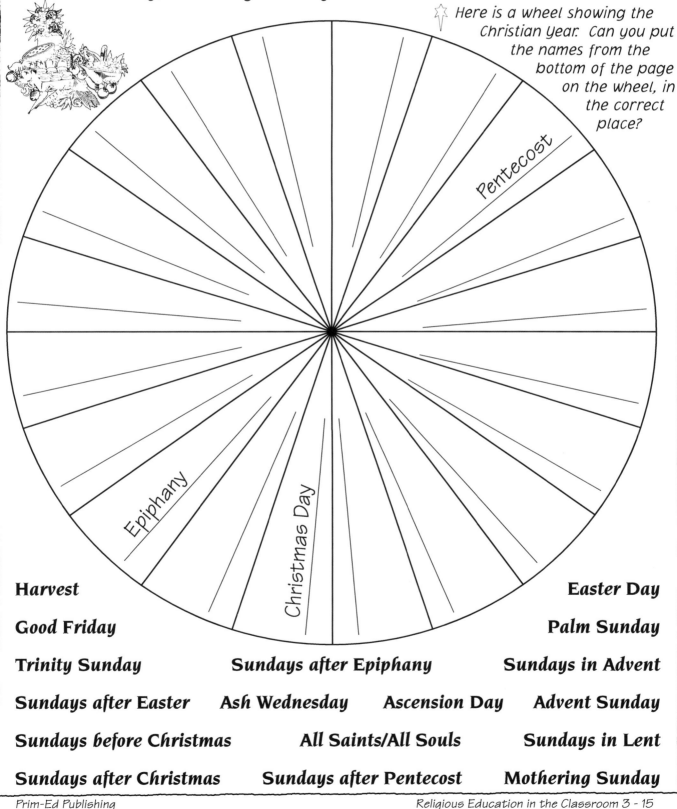

Pentecost

Epiphany

Christmas Day

Harvest

Good Friday

Trinity Sunday

Sundays after Easter

Sundays before Christmas

Sundays after Christmas

Sundays after Epiphany

Ash Wednesday

All Saints/All Souls

Sundays after Pentecost

Easter Day

Palm Sunday

Sundays in Advent

Ascension Day

Advent Sunday

Sundays in Lent

Mothering Sunday

Christian Values

Interview a committed Christian and ask what being a Christian means to them. Discuss their answers in a group. Discuss these Christian values, what do they mean to you and to the others in your group? After your discussion complete the grid.

Value	Definition	What it means to me	What it means to others
Love			
Hope			
Charity			
Friendship			
Acceptance			
Honour			

A Christian Organisation

☆ Choose a Christian organisation and find out as much as you can about it.
Interview someone from the organisation and ask them a series of questions.
Interview someone the organisation helps, ask them what they think of the organisation.
Discuss your findings then complete this table.

Name of Organisation: _____

Activities undertaken by the organisation	People from the organisation who undertake the activities	People from the community who are helped by the activities	Christian values which are central to the activity

The Apostles' Creed

Christian beliefs are summarised in the 'creed'. The word 'creed' comes from Latin and means 'belief'. There are two important creeds, the Apostles' Creed and the Nicene Creed. They are used by Christians all over the world. They say the creeds during worship to reaffirm their beliefs.

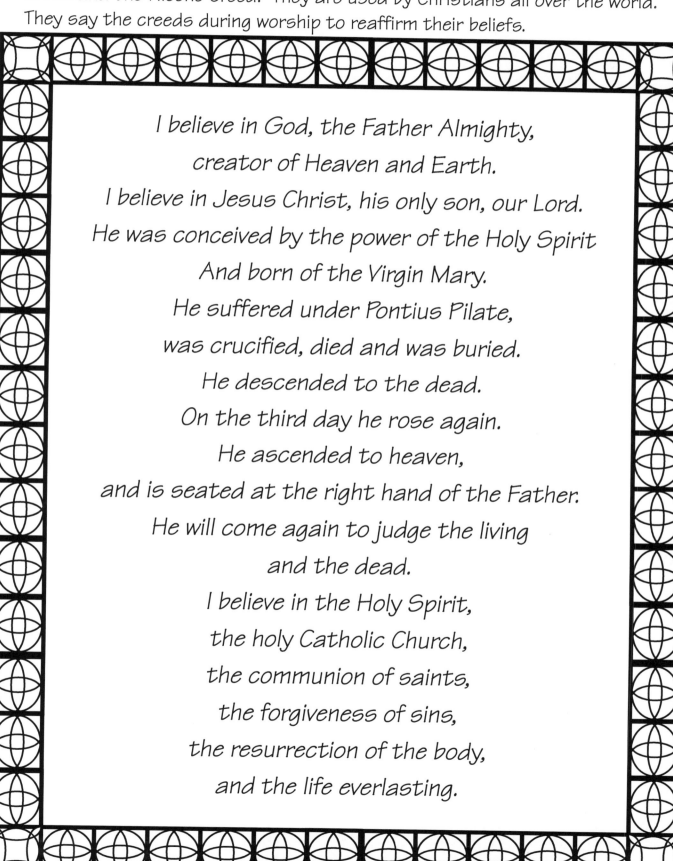

I believe in God, the Father Almighty,
creator of Heaven and Earth.
I believe in Jesus Christ, his only son, our Lord.
He was conceived by the power of the Holy Spirit
And born of the Virgin Mary.
He suffered under Pontius Pilate,
was crucified, died and was buried.
He descended to the dead.
On the third day he rose again.
He ascended to heaven,
and is seated at the right hand of the Father.
He will come again to judge the living
and the dead.
I believe in the Holy Spirit,
the holy Catholic Church,
the communion of saints,
the forgiveness of sins,
the resurrection of the body,
and the life everlasting.

Saint Francis of Assisi

Saints were people who lived especially good lives. Their lives were good examples of how to lead a Christian life. One of the best-loved saints is Saint Francis of Assisi.

☆ *Using the words below, complete this passage.*

Francis was born in the town of Assisi in _____[1], about 800 years ago. He was the son of a _____[2] merchant and had a very comfortable life. However, he felt that _____[3] was telling him to live a

_____[4] life. He left his home with no possessions except the _____[5] he wore. He lived a very simple life, he wore only simple clothes, had no _____[6] and often slept in the open air. He travelled around caring for the poor and the _____[7], and telling people about Jesus' teachings. He _____[8] his life and seemed to always be happy.

He was joined by other men who _____[9] his view and from this group the Franciscan order of _____[10] begun. The Franciscans still exist _____[11], _____[12] for the sick and the

_____[13]. Saint Francis is remembered as a _____[14] man who cared not just about people, but about all the _____[15] and

_____[16]. He saw everything in the world as being part of God's

_____[17].

enjoyed	different	rich	birds	friars	God
caring	furniture	creation	robe	Italy	poor
today	animals	shared	sick	holy	

What are the most important lessons Saint Francis has to teach us?

_____

_____

Committed Christians

Here are the names of two committed Christians, whose belief in God helped them to help others. Find out about their lives, then write two sentences in each box to say how they used their Christian beliefs to help others.

Bishop Desmond Tutu

_____

_____

_____

_____

Martin Luther King

_____

_____

_____

_____

In this box, write the name of a committed Christian in your community. Write two sentences to say how they use their Christian beliefs to help others.

_____

_____

_____

_____

_____

Buddha

Buddhism began nearly 2 500 years ago. It was begun by an Indian prince called Siddhartha Gautama. He was a famous teacher who tried to help people to live better lives.

After listening to the story of Buddha, answer the following questions.

1. Why didn't Siddhartha Gautama go out into the world for the first 35 years of his life?

   _____

2. When he did go out into the world, he saw four things. What did the first three things he saw make him think?

   _____

   _____

3. What did the fourth thing he saw make him think about?

   _____

   _____

4. What did these four trips make him decide to do?

   _____

   _____

5. What did Buddha learn during his first six years in the world?

   _____

   _____

6. How did he try to help other people to learn what he had learned?

   _____

   _____

7. Buddha means 'the awakened one' or 'the enlightened one'. Do you think he deserved this title?

   _____

   _____

8. Buddha believed that we should try to decrease suffering in the world for all living things. Discuss how you can do this in your life.

The Five Promises

There are no rules in Buddhism. Buddhists try to think about the results of their actions. This makes them try to always make sensible choices.

To help them make sensible choices they keep simple rules of conduct and make five promises called the five precepts.

Look at each of the five precepts. Write down what you would do in your life to keep these promises.

The Five Precepts	What they would mean in my life
Not to harm any living thing	
Not to take what is not given	
Not to live in an over-excited way	
Not to say unkind things	
Not to take drugs or drink which will cloud the mind	

Buddhist Teachings

Buddhists do not believe in a god. Buddha helped them to see the way, but he is not a god. Also Buddhists do not 'pray' as other religions do. Buddhists seek enlightenment within themselves in a number of different ways.

Here are some ways in which Buddhists look for enlightenment. Match the pictures to the correct captions.

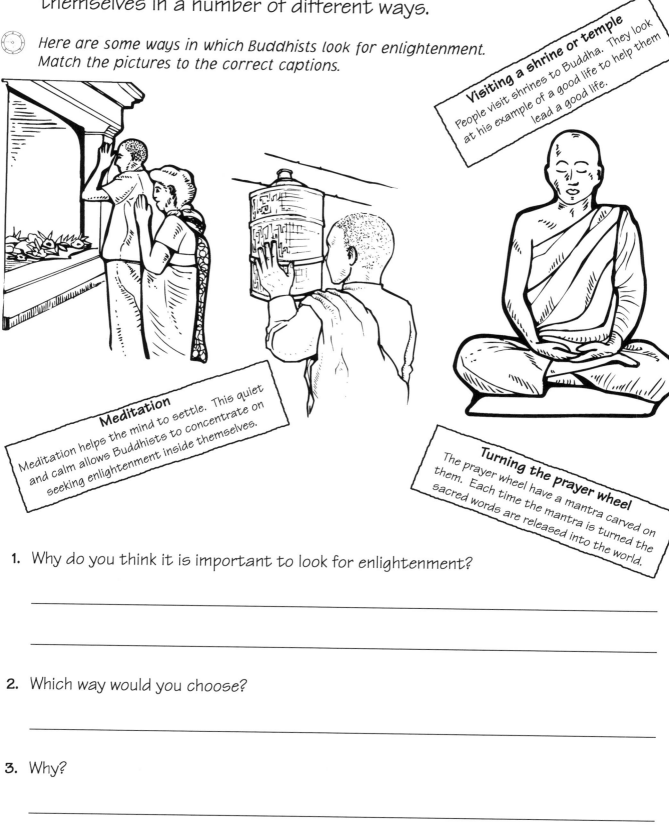

Visiting a shrine or temple
People visit shrines to Buddha. They look at his example of a good life to help them lead a good life.

Meditation
Meditation helps the mind to settle. This quiet and calm allows Buddhists to concentrate on seeking enlightenment inside themselves.

Turning the prayer wheel
The prayer wheel have a mantra carved on them. Each time the mantra is turned the sacred words are released into the world.

1. Why do you think it is important to look for enlightenment?

_____

_____

2. Which way would you choose?

_____

3. Why?

_____

Buddhist Pilgrimage

As Buddha spent most of his life in India, many Buddhist pilgrims come to the places which were important in his life.

Here are descriptions of the four places of pilgrimage. Match the description to the place names below. Label each place on the map.

Kushinagara

Buddha was born here. It is in Nepal near the town of Kapelavastu. King Ashoka set up a stone pillar to mark the event.

This is the place where Buddha died. It is on the banks of the River Ganges.

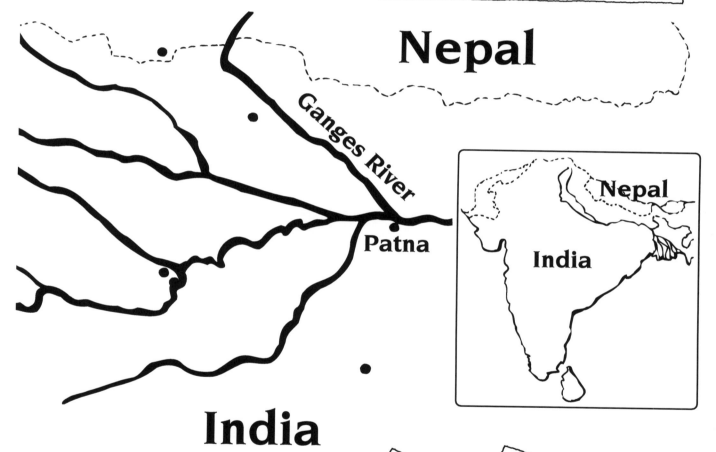

Nepal

Ganges River

Patna

India

Here Buddha preached his first sermon in a deer park. The deer park still exists and there is a large stupa built by King Ashoka. It is now a suburb of the city Varanasi.

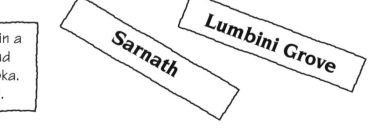

Sarnath

Lumbini Grove

Bodh Gaya

A descendant of the famous Bodhi Tree grows beside the temple. The tree often has many colourful prayer flags in its branches. The temple celebrates the place where Buddha was enlightened.

Hindu Gods and Goddesses

Hindus believe that there is one supreme god, the creation god, Brahman. Brahman can be known and represented in many different ways. The other gods and goddesses in the Hindu religion are all parts of Brahman. Each of these other gods and goddesses have their own appearance and they are each known for different qualities.

ॐ *Here are some of the Hindu Gods and Goddesses.*
Can you match the labels to the correct illustration?

Krishna
He was a mischievous child who became a saviour.

Brahma
He is the creator and has four heads to see in all directions.

Vishnu and Lakshmi
Vishnu is the preserver of life. His wife Lakshmi is the goddess of wealth and beauty.

Shiva
Shiva is often shown as Lord of the Dance. He dances through life and death.

Kali
She is the destroyer of evil.

Ganesha
He is the elephant-headed god of success.

Rama and Sita
They represent the ideal male and female behaviours. They are celebrated at Divali.

Hinduism

Hinduism is the oldest religion. It probably began in the Indus Valley over 4 000 years ago and because the religion is so old, it has changed and it incorporates many different ideas. It includes some ideas from other religions.

To show how one religion can incorporate many different ideas, Hindus tell this story about the Elephant and the Blind Men.

A group of blind men wanted to find out what an elephant looked like. An elephant was brought in and each of the men touched it and described what they could feel. Each one said that he knew what the beast was like, they were all confident they knew its shape and texture. But each one had touched a different part of the elephant and only knew that part.

Look at the picture and match each of the six people to the description you think best describes the part of the elephant he is touching.

It's like a wall.

It's like a rope.

It's like a spear.

It's like a tree.

It's like a snake.

It's like a fan.

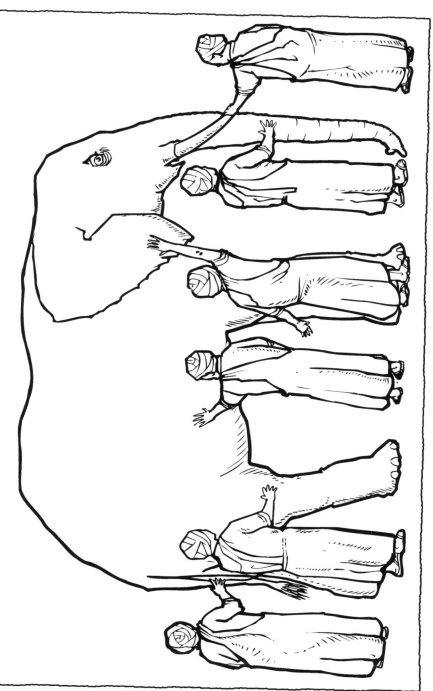

Hindu Worship

ॐ *Can you fill in the spaces with words from the box below?*

Hindus do not have to worship

_____[1] at their Mandir

(temple). They can worship there whenever they want, but

many _____[2] only

_____[3] the temple on holy days and at _____[4] .

When Hindus worship the _____[5] (puja), they offer food and flowers to the

god. The food is _____[6] and then given back to the worshipper. The food

is eaten, knowing that it has been _____[7] with the god.

Hindus worship at home together. Most families have a shrine in their house, if possible in its own

room. Here they keep the _____[8] god. The family do not

worship in dirty clothes and they do not approach the shrine with _____[9] on.

They may _____[10] in the morning, before starting

the day and at night before going to bed.

The shrine will contain objects which

_____[11] the five senses.

This is to involve the

_____[12] person in

the worship.

household	festivals	pray	shoes	whole	Hindus
together	shared	match	visit	shrine	blessed

1. Which of the five senses do each of the objects at the shrine represent?

_____

Benares

Hindu pilgrims come from all over the world to bathe in the River Ganges at Benares. It is the most important place of pilgrimage for Hindus.

ॐ *Can you tell which of these statements are true or false? Circle the correct one.*

1. The sacred river of the Hindus, the Ganges, is a goddess.

True   False

2. Bathing in the River Ganges cleanses pilgrims of their sins.

True   False

3. The River Ganges is sacred only to Hindus.

True   False

4. Pilgrims submerge themselves in the river as part of the ritual.

True   False

5. Hindus cremate their dead and most Hindus would like to be cremated at Benares and have their ashes scattered in the river.

True   False

6. The ghats on the river banks are for decoration.

True   False

7. The best time to bathe is at dawn.

True   False

8. Men and women bathe separately.

True   False

Islam - Prophets and Beliefs

Islam is based on belief in one god called Allah. People who belong to the religion of Islam are called Muslims.

Muslims believe that Allah sent many messengers or prophets with his message. Four of his early messengers were Ibrahim, Musa, Dawud and Isa. Jews and Christians also had their own prophets.

Can you give them the names they have in the Torah and Bible?

	Torah	Bible
Ibrahim		
Dawud		
Musa		
Isa		

The final prophet of Islam and most important was Muhammad. He established the faith of Islam and the angel Jibril revealed the words of Allah to him. These revelations were written into the holy book of Islam, the Qur'an. Muhammad showed Muslims how to live their daily life as Allah had decreed.

The ways in which Muslim beliefs are put into action in daily life are called The Five Pillars of Islam.

Can you match the correct label to each of the descriptions?

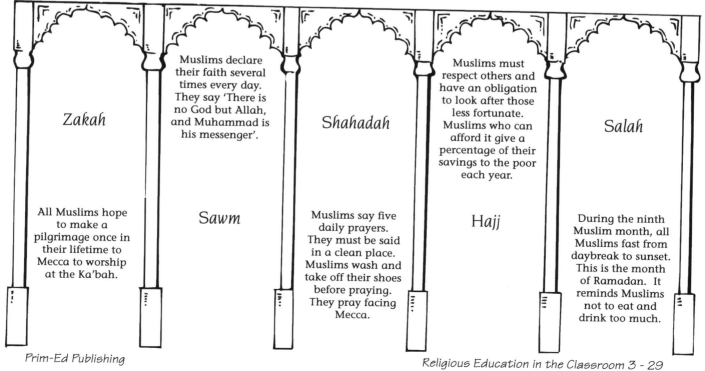

Zakah

Muslims declare their faith several times every day. They say 'There is no God but Allah, and Muhammad is his messenger'.

Shahadah

Muslims must respect others and have an obligation to look after those less fortunate. Muslims who can afford it give a percentage of their savings to the poor each year.

Salah

All Muslims hope to make a pilgrimage once in their lifetime to Mecca to worship at the Ka'bah.

Sawm

Muslims say five daily prayers. They must be said in a clean place. Muslims wash and take off their shoes before praying. They pray facing Mecca.

Hajj

During the ninth Muslim month, all Muslims fast from daybreak to sunset. This is the month of Ramadan. It reminds Muslims not to eat and drink too much.

Muslim Worship

Muslims pray five times a day. Each prayer time has a name.

Fajr - the morning prayer, is said after dawn.

Zuhr - this prayer is said just after midday.

Asr - this prayer is said in the late afternoon.

Maghrib - The Sunset prayer, is said immediately after the sun sets.

Isha - the night time prayer, is said before going to bed.

Muslims must wash in preparation for prayer or worship. This is called Wudu. They always wash in a set order, very carefully so that they are ready to pray. This ritual is performed whether they are going to pray in the mosque or at home.

Can you put these labels in the correct order? Draw a picture in each box.

number ( )

Wash the face three times, from right to left and from forehead to throat.

number ( )

Wash both feet to the ankles.

number ( )

Rub wet palms over the head, from the forehead to the back of the head.

number ( )

Wash the ears with tips of index fingers and thumbs.

number ( )

Wash the right arm, then the left arm from wrist to elbow, three times.

number ( )

Sniff water into the nose three times, then wash the tip of the nose.

number ( )

Put a handful of water into the mouth and rinse it three times.

number ( )

Wash both hands to the wrist, three times.

number ( )

Wash the nape of the neck with the backs of the hands.

The Mosque

The mosque is the place where Muslims go to pray together. The daily prayers are recited in the mosque at the set times by the mu'adhin. All male Muslims are expected to attend the mosque for midday prayers on Friday. Women and men sit separately in the mosque.

Can you draw a line from each label to the correct place on the picture?

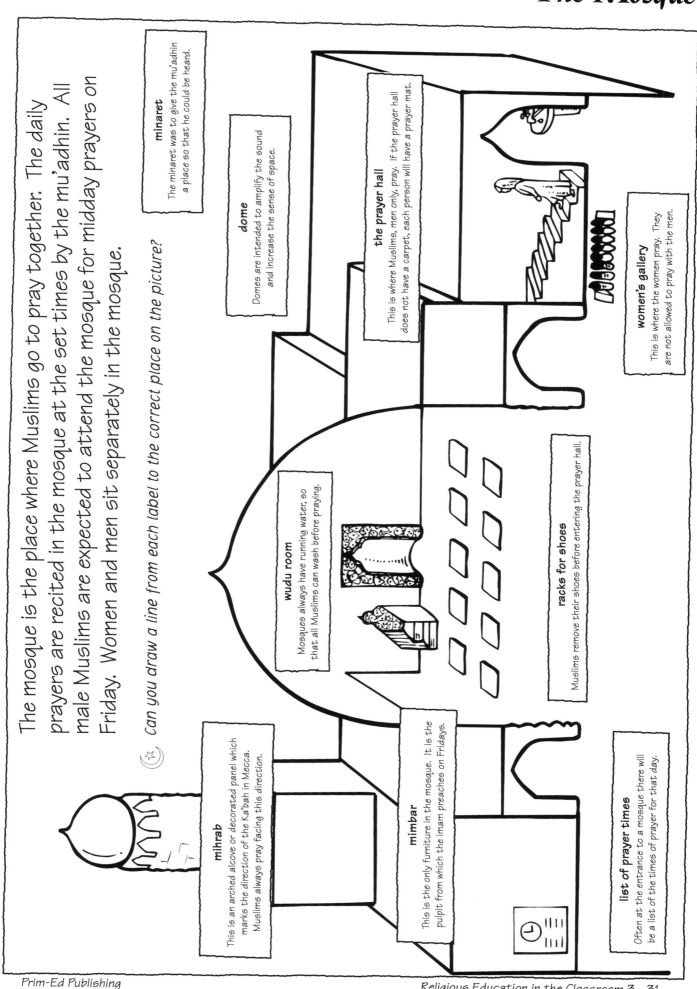

minaret

The minaret was to give the mu'adhin a place so that he could be heard.

dome

Domes are intended to amplify the sound and increase the sense of space.

the prayer hall

This is where Muslims, men only, pray. If the prayer hall does not have a carpet, each person will have a prayer mat.

women's gallery

This is where the women pray. They are not allowed to pray with the men.

wudu room

Mosques always have running water, so that all Muslims can wash before praying.

racks for shoes

Muslims remove their shoes before entering the prayer hall.

mihrab

This is an arched alcove or decorated panel which marks the direction of the Ka'bah in Mecca. Muslims always pray facing this direction.

mimbar

This is the only furniture in the mosque. It is the pulpit from which the imam preaches on Fridays.

list of prayer times

Often at the entrance to a mosque there will be a list of the times of prayer for that day.

The Hajj

All Muslims hope to make the pilgrimage to Mecca once in their lifetime. Mecca is the place of Muhammad's birth. It is also the place where he drove out the false gods and restored the Ka'bah to the worship of Allah only.

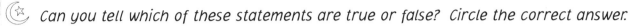 *Can you tell which of these statements are true or false? Circle the correct answer.*

1. When Muhammad went to Mecca he built a new shrine for Allah.
   True   False

2. Pilgrims approach Mecca with a guide, to make sure they know the rites of the hajj.
   True   False

3. Pilgrims go to Mecca to follow in Muhammad's footsteps.
   True   False

4. When pilgrims arrive in Mecca they go to the Ka'bah and walk around it seven times.
   True   False

5. Pilgrims wear their best clothes when they go on the hajj.
   True   False

6. During the hajj, the festival of Eid-al-Adha is celebrated.
   True   False

7. The hajj takes place in the month before Ramadan.
   True   False

8. Those who go on the hajj must provide for those who cannot go in their absence.
   True   False

9. Whole families go on the hajj together.
   True   False

Prophets and Teachers

There are many prophets and teachers in the Jewish religion. Their stories are all in the Jewish Bible.

✡ Look up each of these prophets and teachers and read their story. Write in the table what you think is the most important act in their lives and what that means to the Jews.

Prophet or Teacher	Important incident	Relevance to me
Abraham		
Isaac		
Moses		
David		
Solomon		
Elijah		

Jewish Customs and Traditions

✡ *Can you match these important customs and traditions by labelling their descriptions?*

Sabbath   **Rosh Hashanah**   **Bat Mitzvah**

Yom Kippur   **Seder**   **Bar Mitzvah**

1. _____

This is the most sacred day in the Jewish year. It comes ten days after the New Year. Jews fast all day and pray to God, asking for forgiveness for any wrongdoing.

2. _____

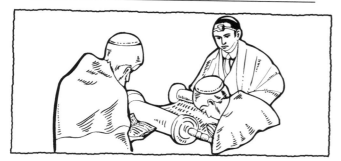

When a boy is 13 he has reached an important time in his religious life. He will now be responsible for his own actions. He will have been studying the Torah. There is a ceremony when he will become a 'son of the covenant'.

3. _____

This is an important ceremony to celebrate the Passover. Each part of the ceremony has a special meaning. The whole family participates in the ceremony.

4. _____

When a girl is 12 she is growing up and will now be responsible for her own actions. She can now share in the religious life and she will be able to read the Torah. There is a special ceremony when she will become a 'daughter of the covenant'.

5. _____

This time begins at sunset on Friday and lasts until sunset on Saturday. The meal on Friday night is prepared in advance. It is a special family occasion. It is a day of rest for the family. Sometime people go to the synagogue during the day. A ceremony at home ends the day.

6. _____

At this important festival the shofar is sounded. This is to remind people that it is a New year and that they should prepare to lead better lives.

The Synagogue

The synagogue is a meeting place for the Jewish community. It is the place where the Torah is kept and where Jews go to pray together. The worship is mainly prayers and readings from the Torah. It is often led by a rabbi or a cantor. Jews often go to the synagogue during the Sabbath. In some synagogues women and men sit separately.

✡ Can you draw a line from each label to the correct place on the picture?

bimah
This is a raised platform from which the Torah scroll is read.

Star of David
This six pointed star is an important symbol and will be seen inside and outside synagogues.

the parochet
This is the curtain which hangs in front of the ark. The colour of the curtain may change for festivals.

the tamid
This is a perpetual light, traditionally an oil lamp.

seats for the congregation
These seats all face the bimah, not the ark.

pulpit
This is the place from which the rabbi speaks for the congregation.

women's gallery
In some synagogues women sit separately from the men.

the ark
This is a cupboard in which the Torah scroll is kept. It is named after the Ark of the Covenant in the first temple, which contained the Ten Commandments.

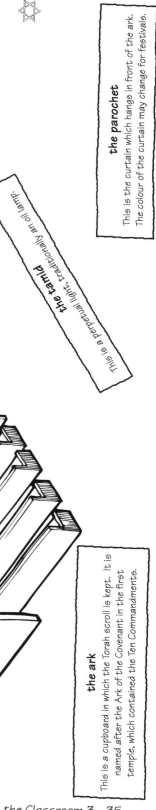

Clothes for Prayer

Many Jews wear special clothes when they pray.

✡ Can you name the special articles in this picture? Write the name of each article in the box and an explanation of their importance.

1. _____

_____

_____

_____

2. _____

_____

_____

3. _____

_____

_____

_____

Sikh Gurus

The first Sikh Guru was Guru Nanak. He was born a Hindu but he felt there was a better way. After travelling and teaching in India and the Middle East he started a new religion in which everyone is equal.

He was the first 'Guru'. Guru means holy man or teacher. He was followed by nine more Gurus and then the writing of Sikhism which has become the 11th and last Guru.

Can you find the names of all eleven Gurus in this wordsearch?

l	u	s	t	c	n	t	r	p	o	v	s
g	g	o	b	r	s	e	t	n	a	a	a
g	o	b	a	n	v	g	l	a	m	k	n
k	b	i	h	a	s	h	t	n	a	r	g
r	i	k	a	h	g	b	p	a	r	a	a
s	n	r	b	s	u	a	g	k	d	m	d
a	d	i	r	i	r	h	t	k	a	d	f
j	s	s	a	r	j	a	n	l	s	a	e
b	i	y	n	k	g	d	s	r	n	s	n
i	n	b	a	r	u	u	p	q	s	r	u
d	g	i	n	a	r	r	j	g	m	s	p
u	h	n	s	h	a	r	r	a	if	a	c
b	s	i	d	b	g	a	u	s	n	a	n
h	a	r	g	o	b	i	n	d	r	p	k

1. Which Guru founded the holy city of Amritsar?

   _____

2. Which Guru built the Golden Temple at Amritsar?

   _____

3. Which Guru founded the Sikh brotherhood called the Khalsa?

   _____

4. Which Guru developed a written script for Punjabi?

   _____

The Khalsa

During their history, the Sikhs have been persecuted in India. Two of the Gurus were put to death for their beliefs. The tenth Guru, Guru Gobind Singh, decided to found the Khalsa, a Sikh brotherhood. It was to help resist persecution.

Today Sikhs choose to join this brotherhood to affirm their beliefs. There is a special ceremony, the Amrit, which is an initiation into the Khalsa.

Use the reference books in your library to answer these questions about the Khalsa.

1. When do Sikhs join the Khalsa?

   _____

   _____

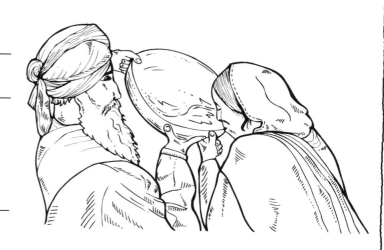

2. Are there any restrictions on membership of the Khalsa?

   _____

   _____

3. Where does the Amrit take place?

   _____

4. What happens at the Amrit?

   _____

   _____

5. What changes in a persons life when they join the Khalsa?

   _____

6. What happened at the first Amrit?

_____

A Sikh temple is called a gurdwara which means 'door to the Guru'. It is an important centre for the Sikh community as well as a place of worship. It contains meeting rooms and classrooms. Everyone sits on the floor; only the Guru Granth Sahib is raised.

Can you draw a line from each label to the correct place on the picture?

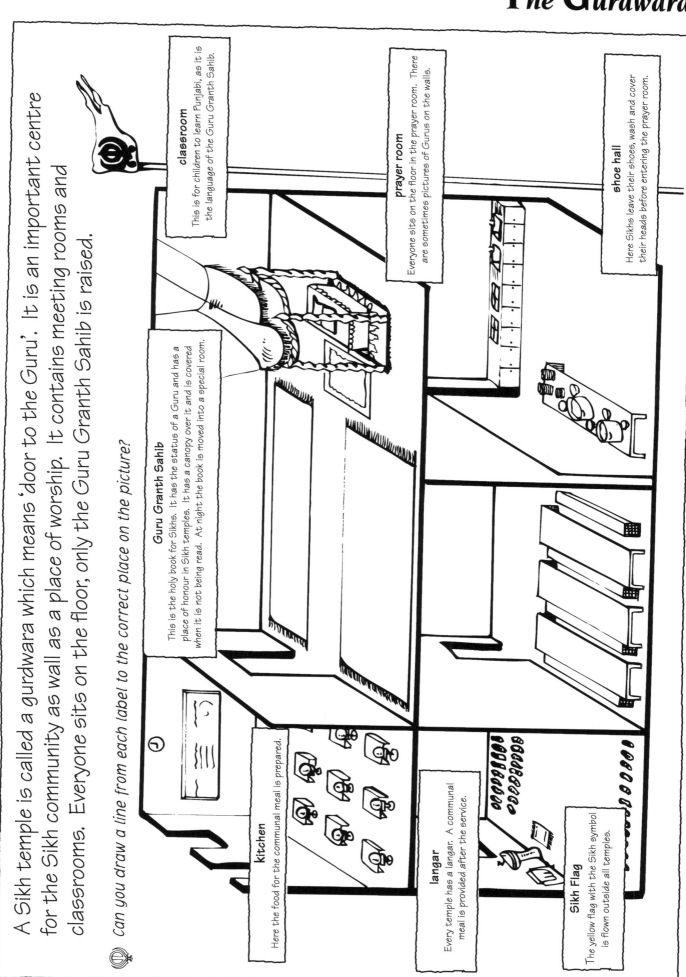

classroom

This is for children to learn Punjabi, as it is the language of the Guru Granth Sahib.

prayer room

Everyone sits on the floor in the prayer room. There are sometimes pictures of Gurus on the walls.

shoe hall

Here Sikhs leave their shoes, wash and cover their heads before entering the prayer room.

Guru Granth Sahib

This is the holy book for Sikhs. It has the status of a Guru and has a place of honour in Sikh temples. It has a canopy over it and is covered when it is not being read. At night the book is moved into a special room.

kitchen

Here the food for the communal meal is prepared.

langar

Every temple has a langar. A communal meal is provided after the service.

Sikh Flag

The yellow flag with the Sikh symbol is flown outside all temples.

The temple at Amritsar is the most important holy place of the Sikhs.

Can you tell which of these statements are true or false? Circle the correct answer.

1. Guru Nanak had a pool built at Amritsar.

True   False

2. Guru Arajan, the fifth Guru, had a temple built in the middle of the pool.

True   False

3. Pilgrims who visit Amritsar bathe in the pool before entering.

True   False

4. The Guru Granth Sahib is not read in this temple.

True   False

5. Verses from the Guru Granth Sahib are written on the walls.

True   False

6. The temple was re-built in marble in the 20th century.

True   False

7. The Guru Granth Sahib is kept in a special gateway and brought to the temple in a casket each day.

True   False

8. This was to show that everyone can enter and all should be humble before God.

True   False

9. It is now known as the marble temple.

True   False

10. It was different to a Hindu temple because people do not climb steps to the worship room.

True   False

Glossary -
Buddhism

Write the definitions of each item.

Bodhi Tree _____

Buddha _____

Dharma _____

Dukka _____

Eight-fold Path _____

Five precepts _____

Four noble truths _____

Karma _____

Meditation _____

Nirvana _____

Sangha _____

Stupa _____

Tripitaka _____

Wesak _____

Zen _____

Glossary –
Christianity

☆ Write the definitions of each item.

Advent _____

Baptism _____

Bible _____

Christmas _____

Disciple _____

Easter _____

Epiphany _____

Gospel _____

Holy Communion _____

Jesus Christ _____

Lent _____

Pentecost _____

Resurrection _____

Reconciliation _____

Trinity _____

Glossary -
Hinduism

🕉 Write the
definitions of
each item.

Arti _____

Ashramas _____

Aum _____

Brahman _____

Divali _____

Dharma _____

Karma _____

Krishna _____

Mahabharata _____

Mandir _____

Puja _____

Ramayana _____

Samskaras _____

Vedas _____

Vishnu _____

Allah

Hajj

Eid-al-Fitr

Imam

Mecca

Mosque

Muezzin

Muhammad

Qur'an

Ramadam

Salah

Sawm

Shahadah

Wudu

Zakah

Glossary - Judaism

✡ write the definitions of each item.

Bar Mitzvah _____

Bat Mitzvah _____

Hanukkah _____

Kippah _____

Kosher _____

Passover _____

Rabbi _____

Seder _____

Shabbat _____

Synagogue _____

Tallit _____

Tenakh _____

Tefillin _____

Torah _____

Glossary –
Sikhism

Write the definitions of each item.

Amrit ceremony _____

Baisakhi _____

Gurdwara _____

Gurpurb Guru _____

Guru Granth
Sahib _____

Kachha _____

Kanga _____

Kara _____

Kes _____

Khalsa _____

Khanda _____

Kirpan _____

Langar _____

Sewa _____

World Religions –
Books and Writings

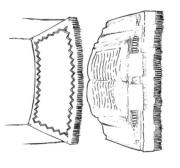

Most religions have sacred books or writings to which people can refer. Three of the religions in this book are called the 'Religions of the Book' – Christianity, Islam and Judaism.

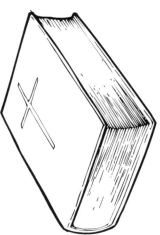

☆ Place the books or writing at the bottom of the page in their correct place in the table. Write a description of the book or writing in the right-hand column.

Religion	Book or Writing	Description
Buddhism		
Christianity		
Hinduism		
Islam		
Judaism		
Sikhism		

Qur'an   Vedas   Torah   Tripitaka   Bible   Guru Granth Sahib

World Religions ~
Festivals

Festivals are a very important part of religious worship for all religions.

From the list of festivals at the bottom of the page choose one for each religion and write a description of it.

Religion	Festival	Description
Buddhism		
Christianity		
Hinduism		
Islam		
Judaism		
Sikhism		

Eid-al-Fitr   Baisakhi   Easter   Wesak   Rosh Hashanah   Eid-al-Adha
Christmas   Hanukah   Divali   Holi   Raksha Bandhan   Festival of the Sacred Tooth

Answers

Page 2 The Christmas Story
LUKE 2:1–20:
1. Jesus
2. Bethlehem
3. Stable with manger
4. No room at the inn/Joseph in Bethlehem for the Roman census
5. Shepherds
6. On the day he was born
7. Yes
8. By angels
9. Good news from Heaven that the baby is born

MATTHEW 2:1–12:
1. Jesus
2. Bethlehem
3. House
4. The Prophets said the Messiah would be born there
5. Men from the East who studied the stars
6. 'Soon afterwards'
7. No
8. Answer not applicable
9. Jesus is the Messiah

Page 5 The Disciples Word Grid
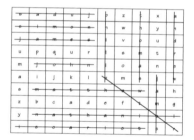

Page 7 The Bible
1. Christians
2. churches
3. congregation
4. study
5. speaks
6. collection
7. four
8. Israelites
9. beginning
10. Abraham
11. promised
12. three
13. worship
14. Gospels
15. Jesus
16. Apostles
17. English
18. Tudor
19. versions
20. James

Page 8 The Books of the Bible
Letters: Romans, 1 Corinthians, 2 Corinthians, Galations, Ephesians, Philippians, Colossians, 1 Thessalonians, 2 Thessalonians, 1 Timothy, 2 Timothy, Titus, Philemon, Hebrews, James, 1 Peter, 2 Peter, 1 John, 2 John, 3 John, Jude.
Prophecy: Revelation.
History: Matthew, Mark, Luke, John, Acts.
Prophecy: Isaiah, Jeremiah, Lamentations, Ezekiel, Daniel, Hosea, Joel, Amos, Obadiah, Jonah, Micah, Nahum, Habakkuk, Zephaniah, Haggai, Zechariah, Malachi.

Wisdom: Genesis, Exodus, Leviticus, Numbers, Deuteronomy.
History: Joshua, Judges, Ruth, 1 Samuel, 2 Samuel, 1 Kings, 2 Kings, 1 Chronicles, 2 Chronicles, Ezra, Nehemiah, Esther.
Law: Job, Psalms, Proverbs, Ecclesiastes, Song of Solomon.

Page 10 New Testament Stories
Mark 5: Daughter of Ja'irus.
Matthew 4: Fishers for men.
Luke 19: Zacchaeus the tax collector.
Acts 9: Peter and the lame man.

Page 11 New Testament Places
John 2–Cana, Luke 1–Capermaum, Luke 1–Nazareth, Mark 1–Sea of Galilee, Matthew 3–River Jordan, Mark 11–Jerusalem, Matthew 1–Jericho, Luke 2–Bethlehem.

Page 14 Places of Worship
Anglican–lectern, altar, font
Baptist–pool, pulpit, table
Methodist–organ, 'empty' cross, pulpit
Roman Catholic–tabernacle, confessional, statues
Quaker–table, Bible, seats 'in the round'

Page 15 The Christian Year
CLOCKWISE, (from 'PENTECOST'):
Pentecost, Trinity Sunday, Sundays after Pentecost, Harvest, All Saints/All Souls, Sundays before Christmas, Advent Sunday, Sundays in Advent, Christmas Day, Sundays after Christmas, Epiphany, Sundays after Epiphany, Ash Wednesday, Sundays in Lent, Mothering Sunday, Palm Sunday, Good Friday, Easter Day, Sundays after Easter, Ascension Day

Page 19 Saint Francis of Assisi
1. Italy
2. rich
3. God
4. different
5. robe
6. furniture
7. sick
8. enjoyed
9. shared
10. friars
11. today
12. caring
13. poor
14. holy
15. birds
16. animals
17. creation

Page 21 Buddha
1. The fortune teller said he should not.
2. The old, sick and dead.
3. The old man – calm and serene.
4. Give up his family, wealth and power and adopt the life of a holy man.

Prim-Ed Publishing

Religious Education in the Classroom 3 - 49

5. He lived the life of a holy man to extreme, as he strove to attain enlightenment. As he almost died, he resumed a normal diet.
6. He became a teacher and preached the 'Middle Way'.

Page 24   Buddhist Pilgrimage

Labels (top to bottom): Lumbini Grove, Kushinagara, Sarnath, Bodh Gaya

Page 25   Hindu Gods and Goddesses

Left–right: Kali, Rama and Sita, Shiva, Vishnu and Lakshmi, Brahma, Ganesha, Krishna

Page 27   Hindu Worship

1. together	2. Hindus
3. visit	4. festivals
5. shrine	6. blessed
7. shared	8. household
9. shoes	10. pray
11. match	12. whole

Page 28   Benares

1. True	2. True
3. True	4. True
5. True	6. False
7. True	8. True

Page 29   Islam–Prophets and Beliefs

1. Torah:
Ibrahim - Arraham
Dawud - David (pronounced Duvid)
Musa - Moshe
Isa - Yeshou/Yeshe

2. Bible:
Ibrahim - Abraham
Dawud - David
Musa - Moses
Isa - Jesus

3. (a) Hajj   (b) Shahadah   (c) Salah
   (d) Zakah   (e) Sawm

Page 30   Muslim Worship

1. both hands	2. mouth
3. nostrils/nose	4. face
5. arms	6. head
7. ears	8. neck
9. feet	

Page 31   The Mosque

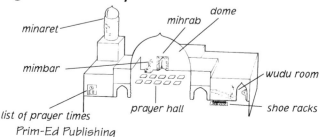

Page 32   The Hajj

1. True	2. True
3. True	4. True
5. False	6. True
7. False	8. True
9. True	

Page 34   Jewish Customs and Traditions

1. Yom Kippur	2. Bar Mitzvah
3. Seder	4. Bat Mitzvah
5. Sabbath	6. Rosh Hashanah

Page 35   The Synagogue

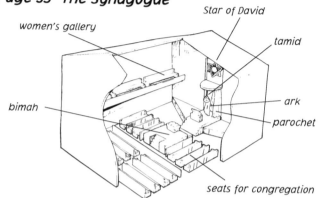

Page 36   Clothes for Prayer

1. tefilah - a black, leather box holding small scrolls with passages from the Bible. One also worn on the arm. Worn to remind person praying to serve God with heart and mind.
2. kippah or yarmulke - a small hat worn by Jewish men, as a mark of respect for God.
3. tallit - a white cloth with fringes and blue stripes, worn at morning prayers.

Page 37   Sikh Gurus

l	u	s	t	c	n	t	r	p	o	v	s
g	g	o	b	r	s	e	t	h	a	a	a
g	o	b	a	h	v	g	l	a	m	k	h
k	r	i	h	a	o	t	t	t	a	t	g
r	k	a	h	g	p	p	k	d	a
s	r	b	s	u	g	k	h	m	d
a	d	i	r	r	n	t	k	a	f
j	s	s	a	j	a	n	l	b	e
b	y	n	k	g	d	s	r	n	b	n
i	b	a	r	u	l	p	q	s	r	u
d	g	i	n	r	r	j	g	m	s	p
u	n	s	t	a	r	a	if	a	c
b	s	i	d	b	g	a	u	s	n	a	n
h	a	r	g	o	b	i	n	d	r	p	k

1. Guru Ram Das
2. Guru Arjan Dev
3. Guru Gobind Singh
4. Guru Angad

Answers

Page 38 The Khalsa

1. When they are ready to fully live up to the high expectations of Guru Gobind Singh.
2. No. All Sikhs are expected to be Khalsa, or working towards that objective. Khalsa means 'pure' and Sikhs have to undergo the sacred Amrit ceremony to gain membership.
3. Usually the gurdwara.
4. Sikhs drink amrit (sugar water stirred with a Sikh sword) and have amrit sprinkled on their eyes and hair, in the presence of five Khalsa Sikhs and the Guru Granth Sahib. Everyone recites the Mool Mantra.
5. Khalsa members:
   • wear the physical symbols of a Khalsa (the 5 Ks) at all times
   • follow the Khalsa Code of Conduct
   • bear Khalsa surnames (Singh for males and Kaur for females).
6. Guru Gobind Singh asked five Sikhs to volunteer to be beheaded, to prove their loyalty to the Sikh faith. He then baptized these five Sikhs and asked the five Khalsas to baptize him.

Page 39 The Gurdwara

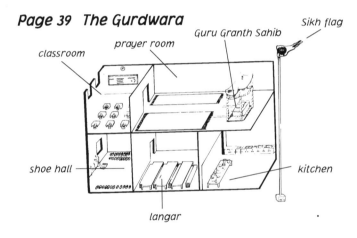

classroom, prayer room, Guru Granth Sahib, Sikh flag, shoe hall, langar, kitchen

Page 40 Amritsar

1. False
2. True
3. True
4. False
5. False
6. True
7. True
8. True
9. False
10. True

Page 47 Books and Writings

Buddhism–Tripitaka
Christianity–Bible
Hinduism–Vedas
Islam–Qur'an
Judaism–Torah
Sikhism–Guru Granth Sahib

Page 48 Festivals

1. Buddhism: Sacred Tooth and Wesak
2. Christianity: Easter and Christmas
3. Hinduism: Divali and Holi
4. Islam: Eid-al-Adha and Eid-al-Fitr
5. Judaism: Hanukah and Rosh Hashanah
6. Sikhism: Baisakhi and Raksha Bandhan